an instant play method that really works!

# UKE'N
# EASY
## UKULELE

by mike jackson

**WISE PUBLICATIONS**
part of The Music Sales Group
London/New York/Paris/Sydney/Copenhagen/
Berlin/Madrid/Hong Kong/Tokyo

Published by
Wise Publications
14-15 Berners Street, London W1T 3LJ, UK.


Exclusive Distributors:
Music Sales Limited
Distribution Centre, Newmarket Road,
Bury St Edmunds, Suffolk IP33 3YB, UK.

Music Sales Pty Limited
4th floor, Lisgar House, 30-32 Carrington Street,
Sydney, NSW 2000, Australia.


Order No. AM1011637
ISBN: 978-1-78558-258-5
This book © Copyright 2016 Wise Publications,
a division of Music Sales Limited.

Created, compiled and edited by Mike Jackson, Diane Jackson Hill
and Flying Wombat Music. Melbourne, Australia 2007.
Cover design by Fresh Lemon (Aus).


Audio Tracks created by Toe Tapper Records.
Mike Jackson – lead vocals, ukulele, mountain dulcimer, harmonica.
Diane Jackson Hill – lead ukulele.
Hugh McDonald – bass, guitar, mandolin, fiddle, banjo, vocal harmonies,
    vocal lead for 'Wildwood Flower'.
Dave Folley – drums.
Michelle Berner – vocal harmonies.
Recorded at Hugh McDonald's Studio, Melbourne, Australia 2007.
Recorded, Engineered and Mixed by Hugh McDonald.


Printed in the EU.

# CONTENTS

# Tuning GCEA

## Methods

### *For good musical ears:*

### Tuning Track (Track 26)

Play the open* strings, starting from the string closest to your head. Turn the tuning peg a little at first, to check which way you turn to make the string higher or lower. Tune the string to the correct note.

\* 'open' means no fingers pressing the strings to the fretboard

### Piano

G - first G above middle C

C - middle C

E - first E above middle C

A - first A above middle C

G C E A

4 3 2 1

### *If you find tuning difficult:*

### Electronic Tuner

Ask the shop staff to help you with the first tune-up. A clip-on tuner is the best option as it takes only the note from the ukulele and is not affected by other sounds in the immediate area.

To remember the notes for tuning the uke: sing 'My Dog Has Fleas'

### Left-Handed Players

The ukulele can be easily changed into a left-handed instrument,
by swapping the two middle strings over. The outside strings are the same thickness so these don't need to be swapped.

Now tune the ukulele to A E C G as shown .

Strum with the left hand and chord with the right.

The finger positions will be the reverse of those pictured for right-handers and your ukulele will face the opposite direction!

Find the left-handed 'instant play' set up at **www.mikejackson.com.au**

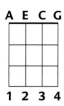

A E C G

1 2 3 4

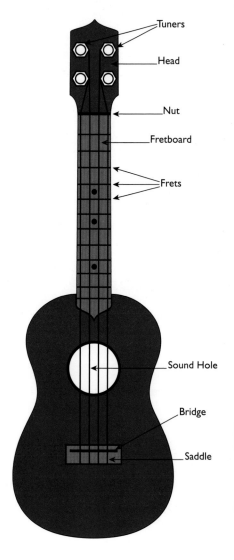

Tuners

Head

Nut

Fretboard

Frets

Sound Hole

Bridge

Saddle

# Mike Jackson's Instant Play Method

This system is simple - but it works! It helps you remember where to place your fingers and makes your chord changes much quicker.

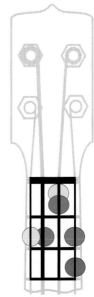

## Setting Up Your Ukulele

1.  Buy a set of sticky coloured paper dots from a newsagency, or office/stationery supplier, and stick them onto the fretboard, <u>underneath</u> the strings, as shown here.

    You'll need red, yellow and green dots.

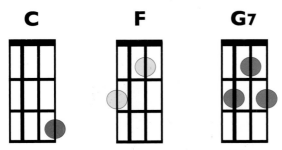

2.  Stick another dot (of any colour) on the back of the ukulele neck — behind the second fret. This is where your thumb goes!
3.  Tune your ukulele — see previous page

## Making Chords

Using your non-dominant hand, gently place your thumb — facing up, on the dot at the back of the fretboard.

Now use the tip of your fingers to gently press the strings onto the correct dots for the chord you are going to play. Make sure you use the correct finger for each dot and that your finger only touches the string that you are pressing down.

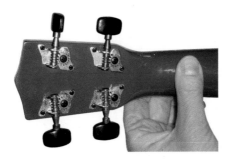

Finger numbering:
1 — index finger
2 — middle finger
3 — ring finger

# Chord Diagrams

## C Chord

Place your ring finger (3)
on the red dot.

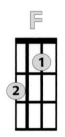

## F Chord

Place your pointer and
middle finger (1 & 2)
on the yellow dots.

## G7 Chord

Place your pointer finger (1)
back on its yellow dot and place
your middle finger (2) and ring
finger (3) on the green dots.

We call this the 'green' chord
even though we use one yellow
dot in it.

## Other chords in this book

### Am

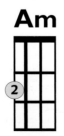

### C7

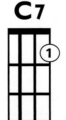

### Dm

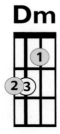

# Strumming

The ukulele, like the drum, must keep the beat so keep your strumming constant through the whole song. Begin by using 'down' strums or a 'down-up-down-up' strum and play with the back of your fingernail/s, side of your thumb, or a felt pick which can be purchased from a music shop.

## Strum patterns (Track 27)

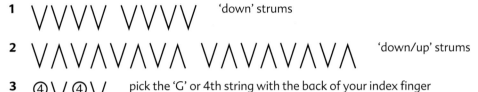

1. ∨∨∨∨ ∨∨∨∨  'down' strums
2. ∨∧∨∧∨∧∨∧ ∨∧∨∧∨∧∨∧  'down/up' strums
3. ④∨ ④∨  pick the 'G' or 4th string with the back of your index finger (the nail) then play a 'down' strum with your fingernail/s

## Chord Patterns (Track 28)

Before playing any songs, try repeating these chord patterns with 4 strums on each chord. If a particular chord change is giving you trouble, slow down your strumming (or play 8 strums on each chord) and practise only that change until you are comfortable with it.

1. F   C   F   C
   ∨∨∨∨ ∨∨∨∨ ∨∨∨∨ ∨∨∨∨

2. C   G7   C   G7
   ∨∨∨∨ ∨∨∨∨ ∨∨∨∨ ∨∨∨∨

3. C   F   G7   C
   ∨∨∨∨ ∨∨∨∨ ∨∨∨∨ ∨∨∨∨

4. C   F   C   G7
   ∨∨∨∨ ∨∨∨∨ ∨∨∨∨ ∨∨∨∨

# Uke'n Play Clues

The play-along audio can be used in many ways:

• To learn the lyrics and melody of the song

• To strum along with quietly while dampening* the strings (to get the strumming hand going)

• Just for fun, choose a '2-chord' song but leave your fingers in the 1st chord position and play only when that chord appears — or have a friend play the other chord in the same way on their own instrument, and alternate!

• Play as much of the song as you can along with the backing tracks — keep strumming even if you don't quite make the chords

• When you are up to speed, try singing and playing along with Mike and the full band

• Then try going solo with the karaoke tracks — for your own interpretations of some of the songs

*to dampen strings — place your fingers, of your chording hand, loosely across all strings so that they do not ring

# ACHY BREAKY HEART

Words and Music by Donald L Von Tress

F
You can tell the world you never was my girl

                                     C
You can burn my clothes up when I'm gone

You can tell your friends just what a fool I've been

                                   F
And laugh and joke about me on the phone

F
You can tell my arms, go back into the farm

                            C
You can tell my feet to hit the floor

You can tell my lips to tell my fingertips

                                F
They won't be reaching out for you no more

    CHORUS:
          F
    But don't tell my heart, my achy breaky heart

                        C
    I just don't think he'll understand

    If you tell my heart, my achy breaky heart

                       F
    He might blow up and kill this man

    INSTRUMENTAL CHORUS

F
Tell your Aunt Louise, tell her anything you please

                         C
Myself already knows I'm not O.K.

You can tell my eyes to watch out for my mind

                         F
It might be walkin' out on me one day

    CHORUS – REPEAT AND REPEAT

*Start with index finger (1) and middle finger (2) on yellow dots*

*... then change to ring finger (3) on red dot*

# PAY ME MY MONEY DOWN

Traditional. This arrangement by Mike Jackson.

C     G7

**CHORUS:**

C                    G7
Pay me, pay me, pay me my money down
                     C
Pay me or go to jail! Pay me my money down

> Try the G7 chord now or have extra practice with chord F on song No.5

C                          G7
I thought I heard the captain say, Pay me my money down
                     C
"Tomorrow is our sailing day." Pay me my money down

**CHORUS:**

C                        G7
Soon as that boat cleared the bar, Pay me my money down
                   C
He knocked me down with a spar. Pay me my money down

**CHORUS**

C                  G7
If I was a rich man's son, Pay me my money down
                     C
I'd sit by the river and watch it run. Pay me my money down

**CHORUS**

C                      G7
Don't need to keep bad company, Pay me my money down
                   C
The Captain stole my wage from me. Pay me my money down

**CHORUS x 2**

> For G7, start by placing your 1st finger, then add your 2nd and 3rd fingers, all on the green dots

# JAMBALAYA

Words and Music by Hank Williams. This arrangement by Mike Jackson.

C      G7

C                          G7
Good-bye Joe, me gotta go, me oh my oh

                              C
Me gotta go pole the pirogue down the Bayou

                        G7
His Yvonne the sweetest one, me oh my oh

                            C
Son of a gun, we'll have big fun on the Bayou

C                            G7
Thibodaux, to Fontaineaux the place is buzzin'

                          C
A kin-folk come to see Yvonne by the dozen

                  G7
Dress in style go hog wild, me oh my oh

                           C
Son of a gun, we'll have big fun on the Bayou

CHORUS:

C                                  G7
Jambalaya and a crawfish pie and fillet gumbo

                                C
For tonight, I'm a-gonna see my ma cher amie-o

                    G7
Pick guitar, fill fruit jar and be gay-o

                          C
Son of a gun, we'll have big fun on the Bayou

C                            G7
Settle down far from town get him a pirogue

                    C
And he'll catch all the fish in the Bayou

                      G7
Swap his mon to buy Yvonne what she need-o

                          C
Son of a gun, we'll have big fun on the Bayou

CHORUS X 2

                G7                        C
Son of a gun, we'll have big fun on the Bayou  (x2)

Strum No.3 on Page 7 goes well with this song

# BUFFALO GALS

Traditional. This arrangement by Mike Jackson.

C
Buffalo gals, woncha come out tonight
G7            C
Come out tonight, come out tonight

Buffalo gals, woncha come out tonight
   G7               C
And dance by the light of the moon

    CHORUS:
    C
    Ain't ya, ain't ya, ain't ya, ain't ya coming out tonight
    G7            C
    Coming out tonight, coming out tonight

    Ain't ya, ain't ya, ain't ya, ain't ya coming out tonight
       G7            C
    To dance by the light of the moon

C
Danced with the dolly with a hole in her stocking
    G7            C
And her feet kept a-rocking and her knees kept a-knocking

Well I danced with the dolly with a hole in her stocking
    G7            C
And we danced by the light of the moon

    CHORUS / INSTRUMENTAL VERSE / CHORUS

Had a little girl with freckles on her face
G7            C
Freckles on her face, freckles on her face

Asked her where she got them, said she got them every place
G7                   C
Ain't ya, ain't ya coming out tonight

    CHORUS x 2

# TOM DOOLEY

Traditional. This arrangement by Mike Jackson.

CHORUS:

F
Hang down your head, Tom Dooley, hang down your head and cry
                                                 C

Hang down your head, Tom Dooley.  Poor boy! You're bound to die
                         F

F
Met her on the mountain, there I took her life
                     C

F
Met her on the mountain stabbed her with my knife
               F

CHORUS

F
This time tomorrow, reckon where I'll be
               C

Down in some lonesome valley hanging from a wild oak tree
               F

> Practise with the F chord again

CHORUS

F
This time tomorrow, reckon where I'll be
               C

Hadn't been for Grayson, I'd have been in Tennessee
               F

CHORUS:

F
Take down my old fiddle, play it as you please
               C

At this time tomorrow, it'll be no use to me
               F

CHORUS

C
Poor boy, you're bound to die  (x 2)
               F

# OLD DAN TUCKER

Traditional. This arrangement by Mike Jackson.

**CHORUS:**

C              F
Get out the way old Dan Tucker
     G7            C
You come too late to get your supper
C              F
Get out the way old Dan Tucker
     G7            C
You come too late to get your supper

> Play the chord pattern C F G7 C with 4 strums on each chord

C                 F
Old Dan Tucker's a fine old man
G7             C
Washed his face in a frying pan
                       F
Combed his hair with a wagon wheel
G7             C
Died of toothache in his heel

**CHORUS**

C             F
Old Dan Tucker, he got drunk
G7             C
Fell in the fire and he kicked up a chunk
                  F
Red hot coal got in his shoe
     G7                     C
Lord bless you, Honey, how the ashes flew

**CHORUS x 2**

# MIDNIGHT SPECIAL

Traditional. This arrangement by Mike Jackson.

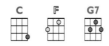

C      F           C
Well, you wake up in the morning, you hear the work bell ring

           G7           C
And they march you to the table, you see the same old thing

        F         C
Ain't no food on the table and no fork up in the pan

       G7              C
But you better not complain, boy, you get in trouble with the man

 CHORUS:
 C       F        C
 Let the midnight special shine a light on me

        G7      C
 Let the midnight special shine a light on me

        F        C
 Let the midnight special shine a light on me

        G7          C
 Let the midnight special shine a ever-lovin' light on me

C         F             C
Yonder come Miss Rosie, how in the world did you know?

         G7         C
By the colour of her apron, the way she wears her clothes

       F          C
Umbrella on her shoulder, piece of paper in her hand

       G7         C
She come to see the governor she wants to free her man

 CHORUS

C       F           C
If you're ever in Houston, well you'd better do it right

       G7      C
You'd better not gamble and you better not fight

       F         C
Or the sheriff will grab you and the boys will bring you down

       G7       C
The next thing you know boy, you're penitentiary bound

 CHORUS x 2

# OH, SUSANNA

Words and Music by Stephen Collins Foster. This arrangement by Mike Jackson.

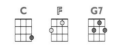

C                                           G7
I come from Alabama with my banjo on my knee
 C                              G7   C
I'm going to Louisiana my true love for to see
                                                                 G7
It rained all night the day I left, the weather was bone dry
 C                                  G7   C
The sun so hot I froze to death, Susanna don't you cry

CHORUS:

F             C                   G7
Oh! Susanna, Don't you cry for me
   C                                     G7   C
I come from Alabama, with my banjo on my knee

C                                           G7
I had a dream the other night, when everything was still
 C                                  G7   C
I thought I saw Susanna, she was coming down the hill
                                                     G7
A buckwheat cake was in her mouth, a tear was in her eye
 C                                  G7   C
Says I, "I'm coming from the south, Susanna don't you cry"

CHORUS

C                                           G7
I soon will be in New Orleans and then I'll look around
 C                                G7   C
And when I find Susanna, I'll fall upon the ground
                                            G7
But if I do not find her, this boy will surely die
 C                                G7   C
And when I'm dead and buried, Susanna don't you cry

CHORUS x 2

# GOODNIGHT IRENE

Traditional. This arrangement by Mike Jackson.

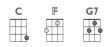

CHORUS:

C        G7              C
Irene goodnight, Irene goodnight
                       F
Goodnight Irene, goodnight Irene
   G7       C
I'll see you in my dreams

      C                 G7
Last Saturday night I got married
               C
Me and my wife settled down
               F
Now me and my wife are parted
    G7              C
I'm gonna take a little stroll downtown

CHORUS

C                  G7
Sometimes I live in the country
               C
Sometimes I live in the town
           F
Sometimes I get a notion
 G7            C
To jump in the river and drown

CHORUS

       C             G7
Stop your ramblin', stop your gamblin'
            C
Quit staying out late at night
              F
Come home to your wife and family
 G7         C
And stay by the fireside bright

CHORUS x 2

# I WALK THE LINE

Words and Music by John R Cash.

C    G7                C
I keep a close watch on this heart of mine
        G7              C
I keep my eyes wide open all the time
       F               C
I keep the ends out for the tie that binds
          G7      C
Because you're mine, I walk the line

C    G7            C
I find it very, very easy to be true
        G7            C
I find myself alone when each day's through
       F             C
Yes, I'll admit that I'm a fool for you
          G7      C
Because you're mine, I walk the line

C    G7              C
As sure as night is dark and day is light
        G7            C
I keep you on my mind both day and night
       F                C
And happiness I've known proves that it's right
          G7      C
Because you're mine, I walk the line

C    G7              C
You've got a way to keep me on your side
        G7            C
You give me cause for love that I can't hide
       F             C
For you I know I'd even try to turn the tide
          G7      C
Because you're mine, I walk the line

REPEAT VERSE 1, REPEAT LAST LINE x 2

# BANKS OF THE OHIO

Traditional. This arrangement by Mike Jackson.

C       G7
I asked my love to take a walk
        C
To take a walk, just a little way
          F
And as we walked, then we would talk
C  G7   C
All about our wedding day

  CHORUS:
  C          G7
  Darlin', say that you'll stay with me
         C
  In our home we'll happy be
          F
  Down beside where the waters flow
     C  G7   C
  Down by the banks of the Ohio

C        G7
I took her by her pretty white hand
        C
I led her down the banks of sand
         F
I plunged her in where she would drown
     C G7   C
And watched her as she floated down

  CHORUS

```
C                              G7
```
Returnin' home between twelve and one
```
                              C
```
Thinkin', Lord, what a deed I've done
```
                         F
```
I've killed the girl I love, you see
```
           C     G7      C
```
Because she would not marry me

```
C                              G7
```
The very next day, at half past four
```
                         C
```
The sheriff walked right to my door
```
                              F
```
He says, "Young man, don't you try to run
```
           C   G7            C
```
You'll pay for this awful crime you've done"

CHORUS, REPEAT LAST LINE

# CIGARETTES AND WHISKEY AND WILD, WILD WOMEN

Words and Music by Tim Spencer (Spencer Vern)

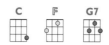

C    F    G7

CHORUS:

    C                      F       C
Cigarettes and whiskey and wild, wild women
                        G7
They'll drive you crazy, they'll drive you insane
    C                      F       C
Cigarettes and whiskey and wild, wild women
                       G7     C
They'll drive you crazy, they'll drive you insane

    C                   F         G7
Well once I was happy and had a good wife
    C                F        G7
I had enough money to last me for life
      C                F        G7
Then I met with a gal and we went on a spree
    C                G7       C
She taught me smoking and drinking whiskey

CHORUS

    C                       F         G7
Cigarettes are a blight on the whole human race
    C               F        G7
A man is a monkey with one in his face
    C                  F        G7
Take warning dear friend, take warning dear brother
      C              G7     C
There's a fire on one end and a fool on the t'other

CHORUS

REPEAT LAST TWO LINES OF CHORUS

# WILDWOOD FLOWER

Traditional. This arrangement by Mike Jackson.

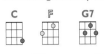

C         G7    C
I used to twine 'mid the ringlets of her raven black hair

         G7  C
The lilies so pale and the roses so fair

          F  C
The myrtle so bright with an emerald hue

         G7   C
And the pale aronatus with eyes of bright blue

C          G7  C
Oh she taught me to love her and promised to love

        G7 C
And to cherish me over all others above

         F  C
When I woke from my dreaming, my idol was clay

       G7  C
All portion of love had flown far away

C        G7   C
Oh I'll dance, I will sing and my laugh shall be gay

        G7  C
I will charm every heart in this crowd I survey

         F   C
How my heart is now wondering no misery can tell

        G7  C
She's left me no warning, no words of farewell

C         G7  C
Oh, she taught me to love her and call her the flower

          G7   C
That was blooming to cheer me through life's dreary hour

        F  C
How I long to see her and regret the dark hour

      G7   C
She left me to pine for my pale wildwood flower

REPEAT LAST LINE

# HOME ON THE RANGE

Traditional. This arrangement by Mike Jackson.

C    F    G7

   C        F
Oh give me a home where the buffalo roam

     C      G7
Where the deer and the antelope play

    C      F
Where seldom is heard a discouraging word

     C   G7  C
And the skies are not cloudy all day

    C       F
Oh, give me a land where the bright diamond sand

    C      G7
Flows leisurely down the stream

     C        F
Where the graceful white swan goes gliding along

     C   G7   C
Like a maid in a heavenly dream

CHORUS:
  C   G7     C
Home, home on the range

             G7
Where the deer and the antelope play

    C      F
Where seldom is heard a discouraging word

     C   G7  C
And the skies are not cloudy all day

     C      F
Where the air is so pure, the zephyrs so free

   C      G7
The breezes so balmy and light

    C      F
That I would not exchange my home on the range

  C  G7  C
For all the cities so bright

CHORUS x 2

# ANGEL BAND

Traditional. This arrangement by Mike Jackson.

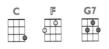

C       F    G7

C            F    C           G7   C
My latest sun is sinking fast, my race is nearly run
                     F      C                G7  C
My strongest trials now are past, my triumph has begun

CHORUS:

G7       C
Oh, come, Angel Band
G7       C
Come and around me stand
F                  C                         G7    C
Bear me away on your snow white wings to my immortal home
F                  C                         G7    C
Bear me away on your snow white wings to my immortal home

C            F   C           G7    C
I know I'm near the holy ranks of friends and kindred dear
                    F   C           G7    C
I brush the dew on Jordan's banks, the crossing must be near

CHORUS

C             F      C           G7    C
I've almost gained my heavenly home, my spirit loudly sings
                    F   C           G7    C
The holy ones, behold they come - I hear the noise of wings

CHORUS

# THINGS ARE COMING MY WAY

Traditional. This arrangement by Mike Jackson.

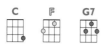

CHORUS 1:

C
I've got the left hind leg of a rabbit
       G7     C
Things are comin' my way

All I got to do is just reach out and grab it
       G7     C
Things are comin' my way

F     G7
Oh me, me oh my

               C
I feel happy all of the time
      G7    C       F
I ain't got nothing to worry my mind
    C     G7     C
Because things are coming my way

CHORUS 1

F        G7
Oh me, how good I feel

               C
I come calling in an automobile
      G7    C       F
I can eat chicken and I don't have to steal
    C     G7     C
Because things are coming my way

CHORUS 1

<pre>
𝔽        G7
Oh me, I feel so fine

                              C
If it starts raining I don't pay no mind
              G7      C          𝔽
Like a pie in the oven or a fruit on the vine
              C      G7      C
You know things are coming my way
</pre>

CHORUS 2:
<pre>
     C
My clothes are tailor made and my shoes are patent-leather
              G7      C
And things are coming my way

All I got to do is just stitch myself together
              G7      C
And things are coming my way
</pre>

<pre>
𝔽        G7
Oh me, me oh my
                    C
I feel happy all the time
              G7      C          𝔽
I ain't got nothing to worry my mind
              C      G7      C
Because things are coming my way
</pre>

CHORUS 1

<pre>
𝔽        G7
Oh me, me oh my
                    C
I feel happy all the time
              G7      C          𝔽
I ain't got nothing to worry my mind
              C      G7      C
Because things are coming my way
</pre>

REPEAT LAST LINE x 2

# BYE, BYE, LOVE

Words and Music by Boudleaux and Felice Bryant

C     F     G7

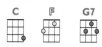

Watch for the rests on the first beat of each F chord in the chorus — before singing

**CHORUS:**

  F        C     F         C
    Bye bye, love,    bye bye, happiness

  F       C                  G7   C
    Hello, loneliness, I think I'm gonna cry

  F        C     F        C
    Bye bye, love,    bye bye, sweet caress

  F       C              G7    C
    Hello, emptiness, I feel like I could die

             G7      C
Bye bye, my love, goodbye

C        G7               C
There goes my baby with someone new

          G7        C
She sure looks happy, I sure am blue

                F          G7
She was my baby 'til he stepped in

                         C
Goodbye to romance that might have been

**CHORUS**

C        G7                    C
I'm through with romance, I'm through with love

          G7         C
I'm through with counting the stars above

              F          G7
And here's the reason that I'm so free

                    C
My loving baby is through with me

**CHORUS**

C     G7     C
Bye bye, my love, goodbye  (x 2)

# STREETS OF LAREDO
# 'COWBOY'S LAMENT'

Traditional. This arrangement by Mike Jackson.

C    F    G7

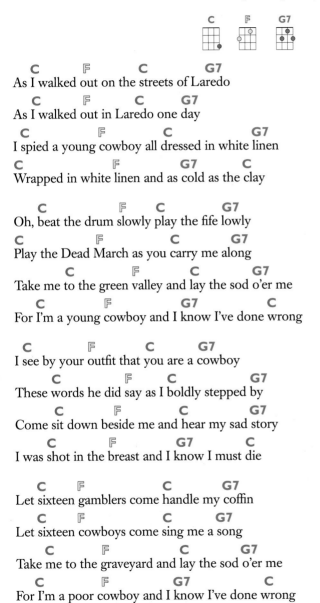

```
C           F         C         G7
As I walked out on the streets of Laredo
C           F         C         G7
As I walked out in Laredo one day
C               F             C               G7
I spied a young cowboy all dressed in white linen
C                 F          G7            C
Wrapped in white linen and as cold as the clay

      C             F       C         G7
Oh, beat the drum slowly play the fife lowly
C           F           C         G7
Play the Dead March as you carry me along
        C           F         C         G7
Take me to the green valley and lay the sod o'er me
      C         F         G7            C
For I'm a young cowboy and I know I've done wrong

      C         F         C       G7
I see by your outfit that you are a cowboy
        C           F       C         G7
These words he did say as I boldly stepped by
        C         F         C         G7
Come sit down beside me and hear my sad story
        C         F       G7          C
I was shot in the breast and I know I must die

      C     F               C         G7
Let sixteen gamblers come handle my coffin
      C     F               C         G7
Let sixteen cowboys come sing me a song
        C         F         C         G7
Take me to the graveyard and lay the sod o'er me
      C         F       G7            C
For I'm a poor cowboy and I know I've done wrong
```

INSTRUMENTAL VERSE, REPEAT 2ND VERSE

Practise the chord pattern first, 3 strums on each chord

Chord pattern:
C F C G7 x 3
C F G7 C

# MORE PRETTY GIRLS THAN ONE

Traditional. This arrangement by Mike Jackson.

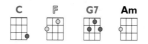

CHORUS:

       C           G7      C
There's more pretty girls than one
F                   C
More pretty girls then one
F               C     Am
Every old town that I rambled round
       C         G7      C
There's more pretty girls than one

C         G7       C
Mama talked to me last night
   F               C
She gave me some good advice
         F                 C    Am
She said, "Son, you'd better quit this old rambling around
    C       G7     C
And marry you a sweet little wife"

CHORUS

C                 G7      C
Honey, look down that old lonesome road
   F                  C
Hang down your pretty head and cry
    F                C    Am
'Cause I'm thinking all about them pretty little gals
    C      G7    C
And hoping that I never die

CHORUS, REPEAT LAST LINE OF CHORUS

# DONEY GAL

Traditional. This arrangement by Mike Jackson.

C    F    G7    Am

**CHORUS:**

**C        Am**
Rain or shine, sleet or snow,

**F                        G7**
Me and my Doney Gal are bound to go

**C        Am**
Rain or shine, sleet or snow

**F                        G7**
Me and my Doney Gal are bound to go

**C            Am**
A cowboy's life is a weary thing

**F                    G7**
For it's rope and brand and ride and sing

*The pattern C Am F G7 repeats all through the song*

**CHORUS**

**C            Am**
Round the campfire's flickering glow

**F                G7**
We'll sing the songs of long ago

**C            Am**
Then we'll ride the range from sun to sun

**F                G7**
For the cowboy's work is never done

**CHORUS**

**C            Am**
Driving the cattle through the fog and dew

**F                G7**
Dreaming of sunnier days and you

**C            Am**
We'll laugh at the rain, sleet and snow

**F                    G7**
When we reach our homes and the folks we know

**CHORUS, INSTRUMENTAL CHORUS**

# MORNING BLUES

Traditional. This arrangement by Mike Jackson.

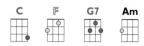

Am   C            Am   C
Woke up early with those morning blues
     Am   C       G7         C
Had an aching head that I wished I could lose
Am        C         Am   C
I looked in the mirror, nearly died of fright
     Am   C         G7         C
Those morning blues, ten times worse than last night

CHORUS:

              F          C G7
I got the morning blues - hurt so bad
Am          C           G7     C
Honey come and love me, they're the worst I ever had
Am          C           G7     C
Honey come and love me, they're the worst I ever had

     Am         C        Am    C
Well a nickel's worth of grease and a dime's worth of lard
Am     C        G7        C
I would buy more but the times is too hard
Am   C         Am   C
I don't see why I have to work so hard
     Am   C         G7       C
I can live off the chickens in my neighbour's yard

CHORUS

     Am      C        Am   C
Well I've been in the army and I've been in love
Am    C    G7  C
I used to fly high like a turtle dove
     Am    C        Am   C
And I've had these blues for just the longest time
Am    C       G7      C
It's just some girl upon this poor boy's mind

CHORUS, REPEAT LAST LINE

# SCARLET TOWN

Traditional. This arrangement by Mike Jackson.

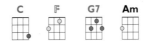

C      G7      **Am**    F    C      G7
Scarlet Town is burning down, goodbye, goodbye
C      G7      **Am**    F    C      G7  C
Scarlet Town is burning down, goodbye Liza Jane

CHORUS:
C                            G7
Ain't you feeling sorry?  Goodbye, goodbye
C                            G7  C
Ain't you feeling sorry?  Goodbye Liza Jane

C  G7  **Am**  F  C      G7
Liza Jane I love you, goodbye, goodbye
C      G7        **Am**    F  C    G7  C
You loved me and my best friend too, goodbye Liza Jane

CHORUS

C  G7     **Am**    F  C      G7
Liza Jane is dead and gone, goodbye, goodbye
C      G7        **Am** F  C    G7    C
But her memories linger on, goodbye Liza Jane

CHORUS

C      G7      **Am**    F  C      G7
Scarlet Town is burning down, goodbye, goodbye
C      G7      **Am**    F  C      G7  C
Scarlet Town is burning down, goodbye Liza Jane

CHORUS x 2

To change from Am to F, add 1st finger on to other yellow dot

# WILL THE CIRCLE BE UNBROKEN

Traditional. This arrangement by Mike Jackson.

C    F    G7   Am   C7

CHORUS:

C                    C7
Will the circle be unbroken

F                C
By and by, Lord, by and by

                      Am
There's a better home a-waiting

C         G7   C
In the sky, Lord, in the sky

C                       C7        F              C
I was standing by the window one dark and cloudy day

                    Am        C     G7      C
When I saw that hearse come rolling for to carry my mother away

                C7           F              C
Well, I told the undertaker, "Undertaker, please drive slow

                    Am         C     G7     C
For this body that you're hauling, Lord, I hate to see her go"

CHORUS

C                   C7         F              C
I followed close behind her, tried to hold up and be brave

                Am          C     G7    C
But I could not hide my sorrow when they laid her in the grave

                 C7          F              C
I went home, our home is lonely now our mother she has gone

             Am        C     G7     C
All my brothers, sisters crying and of comfort they find none

CHORUS x 2

# SHADY GROVE

Traditional. This arrangement by Mike Jackson.

C    Dm

**Dm**      **C**       **Dm**
Wish I was in Shady Grove, sitting in a rocking chair
                **C**      **Dm** **C**    **Dm**
And if those blues would bother me, I'd rock away from there

CHORUS:
**Dm**      **C**       **Dm**
Shady Grove my little love, Shady Grove I say
         **C**      **Dm**   **C** **Dm**
Shady Grove my little love, I'm bound to go away

Try strum No.3 on page 7

**Dm**      **C**       **Dm**
Had a harp, made of gold, every string would shine
       **C**      **Dm**   **C**   **Dm**
The only song that it would play was 'Wish that girl was mine'

CHORUS

**Dm**      **C**       **Dm**
When I was in Shady Grove, heard them pretty birds sing
       **C**      **Dm** **C**    **Dm**
Next time I go to Shady Grove, I'll buy a diamond ring

CHORUS

**Dm**      **C**       **Dm**
When you go to catch a fish, you fish with a hook and line
       **C**      **Dm** **C**    **Dm**
When you go to court a girl, you never look behind

CHORUS

**Dm**      **C**       **Dm**
When I was a little boy, all I wanted was a knife
       **C**      **Dm** **C**    **Dm**
Now I am a great big boy, I'm looking for a wife

CHORUS x 2, INSTRUMENTAL CHORUS x 2

# YOU AIN'T GOIN' NOWHERE

Words and Music by Bob Dylan

**C**    **Dm**    **F**

C          **Dm**
Clouds so swift the rain won't lift
F                C
The gate won't close the railings froze
               **Dm**
Get your mind on the winter time
F          C
You ain't goin' nowhere

> The pattern C Dm F C repeats throughout the song

CHORUS:
  C        **Dm**
Ooh-we, ride me high
     F              C
Tomorrow's the day my bride's gonna come
        **Dm**
Oh my we're gonna fly
F          C
Down in the easy chair

> When changing from Dm to F, just lift off your 3rd finger!

C           **Dm**
I don't care how many letters they sent
     F         C
The morning came the morning went
           **Dm**
Pack up your money pick up your tent
F         C
You ain't going nowhere

CHORUS

C         **Dm**
Genghis Khan he could not keep
F        C
All his kings supplied with sleep
         **Dm**
We'll climb that hill no matter how steep
F      C
When we get up to it

CHORUS - REPEAT VERSE 3 - CHORUS x 2

# About the Authors

Mike Jackson and Diane Jackson Hill have spent a large part of their life inspiring, encouraging and empowering music making in people of all ages.

Mike has sold over 250,000 albums, published many song and dance resources and has performed extensively across Australia and Internationally. His inspirational concerts and workshops attest to his belief that learning to play music is an attainable goal for everyone and that it's never, ever too late — or too early — to begin!

Diane has a Graduate Diploma in Music Education and many years' experience teaching classroom music and taking community music classes for young children.

By using the 'Uke'n Play Ukulele' resource, many — who previously thought of themselves as being 'not musical' — have now fulfilled a lifelong dream of being able to play a musical instrument. Here's what some have said:

> Our ukuleles have had a good workout since the workshop. My wife and I now have uke hour each night after tea and play along with your CD. — Matt

> I joined one of the workshops with a little pink uke I bought for my daughter, plus the book and CD. I am not musical however I am now playing recognizable tunes. — Dean

> On behalf of our little uke group in Footscray, we all wanted to say thank you for your book 'Uke'n Play Ukulele'. It was the book we ALL learnt from and it inspired us!

> I have picked up a copy of the book and CD and have loaned it to my mother, who is learning the uke to get her hands moving. She likes it and I hope I can get it back one day. — Bill

**www.mikejackson.com.au**

**Other books in this series:**

 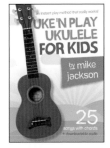 

# HOW TO DOWNLOAD
# YOUR MUSIC TRACKS

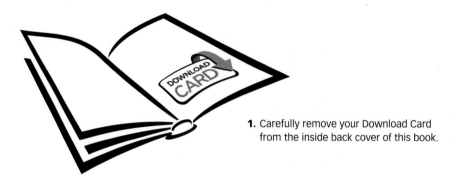

**1.** Carefully remove your Download Card from the inside back cover of this book.

**2.** On the back of the card is your unique access code. Enter this at www.musicsalesdownloads.com

**TO REDEEM THIS CARD VISIT**
www.musicsalesdownloads.com

**ENTER ACCESS CODE:**

**XXXXXXXXX**

Download Cards are powered by Dropcards.
User must accept terms at dropcards.com/terms
which are adopted by The Music Sales Group.
Not redeemable for cash. Void where prohibited or restricted by law.

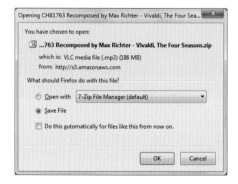

**3.** Follow the instructions to save your files to your computer*. That's it!

*Appearance of download manager will vary depending upon operating system and web browser.
In case of difficulty when downloading files, please contact dropcards.com/help
Card missing? Please contact music@musicsales.co.uk